The
Bank Raid

Brown and Brown

Publishers: Brown and Brown,
            Keeper's Cottage,
            Westward,
            Wigton
            Cumbria CA7 8NQ
            Tel. 016973 42915

First published 1998
Reprinted 2001 & 2004

ISBN 1 870596 67 6

Printed by Reed's Ltd., Penrith, Cumbria on 100% recycled
paper and card.

Introduction

The Bank Raid is a short story in five chapters, written in the first person by five of the people involved. The story is taken up and advanced a little by each person in turn.

The story of the raid on the bank itself is completed by the end of *Chapter 5*, but the reader is invited to add an extra chapter, to explain if and how the robbers are caught. This can be done either orally or in writing and can then be compared with a suggested version given on *pages 38-41* in **The Bank Raid : Exercises**.

The accompanying book of photocopiable exercises, **The Bank Raid : Exercises**, contains 4 pages of exercises for each chapter, and 10 pages of general exercises to be undertaken after reading the whole book.

Please note: *This book,* **The Bank Raid***, may not be photocopied.*

Chapter 1

The pensioner

It was last Thursday that it happened.

Thursday is pension day.

I had gone into town early.

Usually I get my pension at the local post office.

But last week I had to get a birthday present for my grandson.

So I went to the main post office.

It's a new one, near the Millwood Centre.

I spent an hour or two going round the shops.

I always like to go to Marks and Spencer.

I don't often buy anything.

These days I can't afford to.

◆◆◆

Later that morning I came back along George Street.

These two lads came past me.

I don't really know why I took an interest in them.

One of them brushed my arm.

But he didn't shove me aside like some
do.

They both kept looking round all the
time.

It looked as if they thought they were
being followed.

Onè of them was carrying a holdall.

Then I noticed they were both wearing
hats and gloves.

Young lads don't often wear gloves these days.

Not on a mild day in October.

I watched them cross the road and go into the bank.

I just had a feeling that they were up to no good.

I think they stopped inside the swing doors.

I couldn't see them very well.

I stood there on the pavement for a bit.

I wasn't sure what to do.

Then I went into the newsagent's nearby.

I told them what I had seen.

The woman there said she would phone the police.

She said it couldn't do any harm.

She told me her son was a policeman.

She rang 999.

They said they would send a police car straightaway.

Chapter 2

The girl in the queue

It was last Thursday that it happened.

I work at the card shop in George Street.

I've only been there a few weeks.

The owner is a friend of my mum.

It's my first job since leaving school.

I was just about to start College when the job came up.

My mum wanted me to go to College but I fancied earning some money.

Mind you, it's not that much.

I do four days in the week, with one day off.

And I work every Saturday.

That Thursday, we were a bit short of change.

Vicky, my boss, asked me to go to the bank to get some £1 coins.

Our usual bank is up by the Station.

But there's another one just along the street, so I went there instead.

It isn't a big bank.

It's just a local branch.

Only two women were serving that morning.

I stood in the queue for about a minute.

I'd got to the front of the queue when it happened.

These two lads came in wearing balaclavas.

I couldn't believe it.

It was like a scene from the telly.

You see those video camera recordings on news and crime programmes.

But you don't ever think that it's going to happen to you.

There was a middle-aged man at the window nearest the door.

One of the lads had a gun wrapped up in a cloth.

He grabbed the man.

He pointed the gun at him and said to the bank clerk,

" Give us the money, or he gets it ! "

I almost burst out laughing !

It was just like an old gangster film.

I don't know why, but I didn't feel very scared.

I could tell that the robbers were very jumpy.

In fact, I'm not sure that they weren't more scared than the bank clerk.

She said, " Don't shoot ! "

She started to put the money from her drawer into a bag.

Chapter 3

The bank clerk

It was last Thursday that it happened.

I've been working at the bank for over twelve years.

I was full-time until my eldest boy was born.

Since then, I've worked part-time.

The bank helped with play schools and nursery places.

Now my youngest has started school full-time.

So I've increased my hours.

I work school hours most days now.

I usually finish at half past three.

We get training about what to do in a robbery.

But somehow you don't ever think it's going to happen to you.

No one in this branch had ever been in one before - not even the Manager.

She's been in banking for almost 40 years.

I haven't really got over it yet.

I don't think I ever will.

I can't stop telling people about it.

I've been off work since it happened.

But I've told the Manager that I'll go back in again tomorrow.

I'm dreading it.

It all happened so quickly.

I was just starting to add up some cheques from a customer.

He was a middle-aged man in a dark suit.

Suddenly, he was grabbed by a lad wearing a balaclava.

There was another lad with him.

The one in front of me had what looked like a sawn-off shotgun.

It was partly wrapped up in a cloth.

He pointed it at the man and said,

" Give me the money, or he'll get it ! "

◆◆◆

I managed to look calm and I tried not to panic.

But I can tell you I was shaking like a leaf inside.

I said " Don't shoot ! "

I remember that my voice was all squeaky !

I started to put the money from my drawer into a bag.

We are told never to try to argue in a robbery.

The bank says that the safety of the staff and customers always comes first.

Then he said, " And all the rest. "

I could see that both the lads were jumpy.

Julie was on the next till.

I put her notes in the bag.

I heard the alarm begin to ring.

The lad with the gun started shouting at me to hurry up.

I felt as if everyone else in the bank was frozen to the spot.

Everyone was watching me.

Chapter 4

The bank robber

It was last Thursday that it happened.

It was Gary's idea.

He planned it all.

He'd met this bloke who could sell us a
lot of E tablets.

But we needed at least £1000.

I didn't really want to do it.

I'd never done a bank job before.

I almost backed out when it came to it.

But I owed Gary a load of money.

Danny was the driver.

He'd nicked a Vauxhall Cavalier that morning.

He was waiting round the corner in King's Square Car Park.

Gary had an air rifle.

He'd sawn the end off.

He said it would look like a sawn-off shotgun if we kept it covered up.

We decided beforehand just to go for all the cash at the counter.

Trying to get everything from the safe wasn't on.

Not with just the two of us and an air rifle !

Gary made us wear gloves.

And we had balaclavas on.

They were rolled up before we got into the bank.

We pulled them down as soon as we got inside the first door.

Gary went straight to the nearest window.

A customer was standing there, being served.

It was a man in a suit, with a briefcase.

Gary grabbed him and said to the bank clerk,

" Give us the money, or I'll shoot ! "

It seemed like hours that we were inside the bank.

Everyone just stood there like statues.

I recognised the girl at the front of the queue.

She was in the same class as my sister at school.

I turned away from her and hoped she wouldn't recognise me.

The bank clerk seemed to be really slow at getting the money together.

Then the alarm went off.

Gary started shouting at her to hurry up.

At last she gave him the money.

He was supposed to give it to me to put in my bag.

Then we were going to walk out with it, all calm and cool.

But, with the alarm ringing all the time, we both panicked.

I shouted, " Run for it ! "

We raced out of the door and along the street.

I knocked into some old man who got in my way.

We got to the corner of West Street to go down to the car park.

Then I saw a police car coming up George Street.

I couldn't believe it.

We made it back to the car but the copper must have seen us.

We heard the siren start off.

Chapter 5

The policeman

It was last Thursday that it happened.

I was in the City Centre.

I was on my way to book a shoplifter in Boots.

I got a call on the radio.

They said that two lads had been acting suspiciously.

Someone had seen them going into a bank in George Street.

They told me to have a look.

They didn't tell me it was an armed robbery !

I didn't even put my siren on.

When I got half way along George Street I saw two lads.

They were wearing balaclavas and running round into West Street.

I'd gone past the turning before I could stop to turn round.

You've probably seen car chases with police cars on the telly.

Well, I can tell you, it's a bit different in real life.

Just imagine.

I was an ordinary copper on my own.

My usual patrol car was in for service.

I had the old back-up car which no one uses if they can avoid it.

It's known at the Station as the 'Noddy Car'.

I had to do a 3-point turn in a busy shopping street.

At the same time I had to radio for back-up.

I then had to try to follow two young lads sprinting along West Street.

I saw them cut across into the back entrance to King's Square Car Park.

I hardly had time to get out of my car.

I couldn't have caught them anyway because of my knee.

I'd twisted it playing soccer a few days earlier.

As I limped after them there was a squeal of tyres.

A red Vauxhall Cavalier went screaming out of the far exit.

They must have had a driver waiting in the car.

I had no chance to see the numberplate.

I called in on the radio and they put out a general call.

The car was found less than 20 minutes later by a patrol.

It had been abandoned.

It was stolen, of course.

The bank raid itself was a real amateur job.

But, for once, we did have bit of luck.

That evening we got a phone call.

Chapter 6

The C.I.D. officer

Imagine you are the C.I.D. officer.

Finish the story from his or her point of view.

This title is one of a series of **Readers with Exercises**.

For details of further titles in the above series and all other publications in our current catalogue, please contact:

Brown and Brown, Keeper's Cottage, Westward, Wigton, Cumbria CA7 8NQ *Tel. 016973 42915*